TRAVEL JOURNAL

F
FRANCES LINCOLN LIMITED
PUBLISHERS

Frances Lincoln Limited
4 Torriano Mews
Torriano Avenue
London NW5 2RZ
www.franceslincoln.com

National Railway Museum Travel Journal
Copyright © Frances Lincoln Limited 2010
This product is produced under licence from National
Museum of Science and Industry Trading Ltd.
Licence no. 0181.
Text © NMSI Trading Ltd. 2010
Images © NRM/Science and Society Picture Library 2010
The National Railway Museum Collection is a registered
trademark No. 2309517. Royalties from the sale of this
book help fund and support the NRM, York.
To buy prints of the images in this diary see:
www.ssplprints.com

A catalogue record for this book is available
from the British Library

ISBN 978-0-7112-3123-8

Printed in Hong Kong
First Frances Lincoln edition 2010

Publisher's Note: The following abbreviations are used
throughout the book: GCR (Great Central Railways); LNER
(London & North Eastern Railway); LMS (London, Midland &
Scottish Railway); SR (Southern Railways).

Front cover: 'Clacton-on-Sea', LNER poster, 1926.
Artwork by Henry G. Gawthorn.
Back cover: 'The Coronation', LNER poster, 1923–47.
'The Coronation', an aerodynamic train, is shown speeding
across the Royal Border Bridge over the River Tweed at
Berwick-upon-Tweed, Northumberland. Artwork by
Tom Purvis.
Title page: 'Yorkshire Coast', LNER poster, 1937.
Artwork by Frank H. Mason.
Below: 'Lowestoft' (detail), LNER/LMS poster, 1933.
Artwork by Arthur C. Michael.

ABOUT THE NATIONAL RAILWAY MUSEUM

The National Railway Museum is the largest railway
museum in the world. Its permanent displays and collections
are the most comprehensive and significant in their field,
illustrating the history of the British railways and railway
engineering from the industrial revolution to the present
day. In addition to the collection, the National Railway
Museum contains a valuable archive which includes a
fabulous collection of advertising posters and railway
memorabilia. The Search Engine library and archive centre
allows visitors access to railway books, magazines and other
archive materials. The Museum offers a changing
programme of events and exhibitions. For more
information visit ww.nrm.org.uk

National Railway Museum
Leeman Road
York, YO26 4XJ
Telephone: 08448 153 139
e-mail: nrm@nrm.org.uk
website: www.nrm.org.uk
24 hour recorded information line: 08448 153 139

Admission free
Open daily: 10 am to 6 pm
(Closed: 24th, 25th & 26th December)

Every journey whether a weekend away or a trip of a lifetime needs some organization and, with a little planning before you set out, valuable time can be saved when you are en route. This journal is the ideal place to list your travel arrangements – train times, flight numbers and other essential information – together with recommendations for places to visit, stay or eat, gathered from friends or guidebooks. Using this book, your time can be as carefully planned or as spontaneous as you wish.

The 'Journal' section is the place to write about your experiences or to make sketches of the places you explore: the sights and sounds, the unfolding landscapes, the people you meet and the discoveries you make.

At the back of the book, you will find conversion tables and information about countries you may visit or pass through, as well as space to keep track of budgets and make a note of useful addresses.

PERSONAL INFORMATION

NAME _____

ADDRESS _____

_____

_____

TELEPHONE _____

MOBILE _____

FAX _____

E-MAIL ADDRESS _____

PASSPORT NO. _____

DRIVING LICENCE NO. _____

MEDICAL INFORMATION _____

_____

_____

IN CASE OF EMERGENCY, PLEASE CONTACT

NAME _____

ADDRESS _____

_____

_____

TELEPHONE _____

MOBILE _____

'The Queen of Scots Pullman', Pullman Company poster, 1930s.
Artwork by Septimus E. Scott.

TRAVEL DETAILS

'The Continent via Harwich', LNER poster, 1933.
Artwork by Reginald E. Higgins.

PLANNING AND PACKING

ITINERARIES

DATES	PLACE
_____ TO _____	_____
_____ TO _____	_____
_____ TO _____	_____
_____ TO _____	_____
_____ TO _____	_____
_____ TO _____	_____
_____ TO _____	_____
_____ TO _____	_____
_____ TO _____	_____
_____ TO _____	_____
_____ TO _____	_____
_____ TO _____	_____
_____ TO _____	_____
_____ TO _____	_____
_____ TO _____	_____
_____ TO _____	_____
_____ TO _____	_____
_____ TO _____	_____
_____ TO _____	_____
_____ TO _____	_____

ITINERARIES

DATES	PLACE

_____ TO _____ _____
_____ TO _____ _____
_____ TO _____ _____
_____ TO _____ _____
_____ TO _____ _____
_____ TO _____ _____
_____ TO _____ _____
_____ TO _____ _____
_____ TO _____ _____
_____ TO _____ _____
_____ TO _____ _____
_____ TO _____ _____
_____ TO _____ _____
_____ TO _____ _____
_____ TO _____ _____
_____ TO _____ _____
_____ TO _____ _____
_____ TO _____ _____
_____ TO _____ _____
_____ TO _____ _____
_____ TO _____ _____
_____ TO _____ _____
_____ TO _____ _____
_____ TO _____ _____
_____ TO _____ _____
_____ TO _____ _____
_____ TO _____ _____

'Clyde Coast' (detail), LNER poster, 1935.
Artwork by Frank H. Mason.

ITINERARIES

DATES	PLACE
_____ TO _____	_____
_____ TO _____	_____
_____ TO _____	_____
_____ TO _____	_____
_____ TO _____	_____
_____ TO _____	_____
_____ TO _____	_____
_____ TO _____	_____
_____ TO _____	_____
_____ TO _____	_____
_____ TO _____	_____
_____ TO _____	_____
_____ TO _____	_____
_____ TO _____	_____
_____ TO _____	_____
_____ TO _____	_____
_____ TO _____	_____
_____ TO _____	_____
_____ TO _____	_____
_____ TO _____	_____
_____ TO _____	_____
_____ TO _____	_____
_____ TO _____	_____
_____ TO _____	_____
_____ TO _____	_____
_____ TO _____	_____
_____ TO _____	_____
_____ TO _____	_____

'Orient-Express', Wagons-Lits poster, c.1940s.

ITINERARIES

DATES	PLACE

_____ TO _____   _____

_____ TO _____   _____

_____ TO _____   _____

_____ TO _____   _____

_____ TO _____   _____

_____ TO _____   _____

_____ TO _____   _____

_____ TO _____   _____

_____ TO _____   _____

_____ TO _____   _____

_____ TO _____   _____

_____ TO _____   _____

_____ TO _____   _____

_____ TO _____   _____

_____ TO _____   _____

_____ TO _____   _____

_____ TO _____   _____

_____ TO _____   _____

_____ TO _____   _____

_____ TO _____   _____

_____ TO _____   _____

_____ TO _____   _____

_____ TO _____   _____

_____ TO _____   _____

_____ TO _____   _____

_____ TO _____   _____

_____ TO _____   _____

ITINERARIES

DATES	PLACE

_____ TO _____ _____

_____ TO _____ _____

_____ TO _____ _____

_____ TO _____ _____

_____ TO _____ _____

_____ TO _____ _____

_____ TO _____ _____

_____ TO _____ _____

_____ TO _____ _____

_____ TO _____ _____

_____ TO _____ _____

_____ TO _____ _____

_____ TO _____ _____

_____ TO _____ _____

_____ TO _____ _____

_____ TO _____ _____

_____ TO _____ _____

_____ TO _____ _____

_____ TO _____ _____

_____ TO _____ _____

_____ TO _____ _____

_____ TO _____ _____

_____ TO _____ _____

_____ TO _____ _____

_____ TO _____ _____

_____ TO _____ _____

_____ TO _____ _____

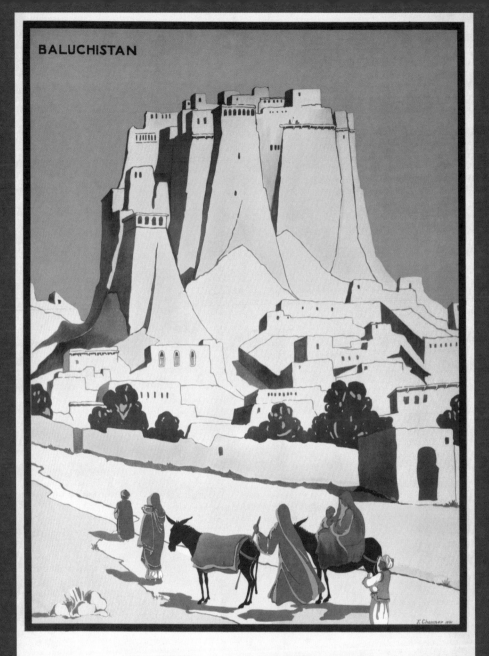

BALUCHISTAN

SEE INDIA

BOLTON FINE ART OFFSET LITHO BOMBAY

DATE	DETAILS

'See India'. Possibly an Indian State Railways poster, 1931.
Artwork by F. Chamber.

PLACES TO VISIT

DATE	DETAILS

PLACES TO VISIT

DATE	DETAILS

PLACES TO VISIT

DATE	DETAILS

PLACES TO VISIT

DATE	DETAILS

'Bridlington' (detail), LNER poster, 1930.
Artwork by Henry G. Gawthorn.

PLACES TO STAY

NAME	ADDRESS AND TELEPHONE NUMBER	NOTES

'Holiday Rivers', LNER poster, c.1930s.
Artwork by Henry G. Gawthorn.

PLACES TO STAY

DATE	DETAILS

PLACES TO STAY

NAME	ADDRESS AND TELEPHONE NUMBER	NOTES

PLACES TO STAY

NAME	ADDRESS AND TELEPHONE NUMBER	NOTES

'Camping Coaches', LNER poster, 1923–47.
Artwork by Frank Newbould.

CAMPING COACHES
IN
ENGLAND and SCOTLAND

ACCOMMODATION FOR 6 PERSONS
RENT £3 PER WEEK

Ask for details at any L·N·E·R Station or Office

PLACES TO EAT

NAME	ADDRESS AND TELEPHONE NUMBER	NOTES

PLACES TO EAT

NAME	ADDRESS AND TELEPHONE NUMBER	NOTES

PLACES TO EAT

NAME	ADDRESS AND TELEPHONE NUMBER

'Visit India' (detail), Indian State Railways poster, c.1930s.
Artwork by William Spencer Bagdatopolos.

PLACES TO EAT

NAME	ADDRESS AND TELEPHONE NUMBER	NOTES

PLACES TO EAT

NAME	ADDRESS AND TELEPHONE NUMBER	NOTES

'Knaresborough', LNER poster, c.1930.
Artwork by Wilton Williams.

JOURNAL

'Express Ease', LNER poster, 1923–30.
Artwork by George Harrison.

Royal Train, 1844. Ink and watercolour depicting the Royal Train, as used
by Queen Victoria for the first royal journey from Euston in November 1844.

JOURNAL

JOURNAL

JOURNAL

JOURNAL

'Holyhead (Holy Island)' (detail), LMS poster, 1923–45.
Artwork by Claude Buckle.

200.000F. de PRIX
E. Montaut
GRANDE SEMAINE
D'AVIATION DE LA
REIMS DU 22 AU 29 AOÛT 1909 CHAMPAGNE
Affiches MONTAUT & MABILEAU 84 Rue d'Amsterdam PARIS

'Grande Semaine d'Aviation de la Champagne', Reims, France, 1909. Coloured lithograph poster by Ernest Montaut advertising the world's first true aviation meeting.

JOURNAL

JOURNAL

'Knaresborough', LNER poster, 1923–47.
Artwork by Henry G. Gawthorn.

JOURNAL

MV Swan on Lake Windermere', 1923–47.
Artwork by Norman Wilkinson.

JOURNAL

JOURNAL

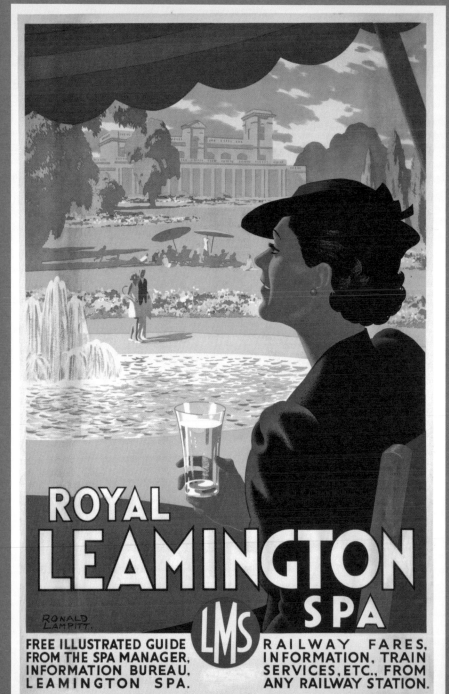

ROYAL
LEAMINGTON
SPA

RONALD
LAMPITT.

LMS

FREE ILLUSTRATED GUIDE
FROM THE SPA MANAGER,
INFORMATION BUREAU,
LEAMINGTON SPA.

RAILWAY FARES,
INFORMATION, TRAIN
SERVICES, ETC., FROM
ANY RAILWAY STATION.

PRINTED IN GREAT BRITAIN BY JORDISON & CO LTD LONDON & MIDDLESBROUGH

'Royal Leamington Spa', LMS poster, 1937.
Artwork by Ronald Lampitt.

JOURNAL

JOURNAL

JOURNAL

'Colwyn Bay' (detail), LMS poster, c.1930s.
Artwork by George Ayling.

'The Coronation Scot Ascending Shap Fell' (detail),
LMS poster, 1937. Artwork by Norman Wilkinson.

JOURNAL

JOURNAL

JOURNAL

JOURNAL

'Bridlington' (detail), LNER poster, 1930.
Artwork by Henry G. Gawthorn.

When winter's here
THERE'S SUMMER
SOUTHWARDS
Go cruising
THE ROYAL MAIL
STEAM PACKET C°

Sanders Phillips and Co., Ltd., THE BAYNARD PRESS, Chryssell Road, S.W.9.

'When Winter's Here, There's Summer Southwards...',
poster, c.1920–40. Artwork by Frank Newbould.

JOURNAL

JOURNAL

'Hints for Holidays', SR poster, 1938.
Artwork by Libis.

"HINTS FOR HOLIDAYS"
"The pull of the South"
Where to go
Where to stay
Over one thousand
Photographs
6D.
At Stations & Bookstalls –
SOUTH RN RAILWAY

JOURNAL

JOURNAL

JOURNAL

JOURNAL

BUDGETS

DATE	DETAILS	AMOUNT	

BUDGETS

DATE	DETAILS	AMOUNT	

BUDGETS

DATE	DETAILS	AMOUNT	

BUDGETS

DATE	DETAILS	AMOUNT	

BUDGETS

DATE	DETAILS	AMOUNT	

BUDGETS

DATE	DETAILS	AMOUNT	

INTERNATIONAL INFORMATION

COUNTRY	DIALLING CODE	HOURS DIFF. FROM GMT	COUNTRY	DIALLING CODE	HOURS DIFF. FROM GMT
Afghanistan	93	+4½	Republic	235	+1
Albania	355	+1	Chad	56	-4
Algeria	213	+1	Chile	86	+8
Andorra	376	+1	China	61	+7
Angola	244	+1	Christmas Island	57	-5
Anguilla	1264	-4	Colombia	269	+3
Antigua and Barbuda	1268	-4	Comoros	242	+1
Argentina	54	-3	Congo	682	-10
Armenia	374	+4	Cook Islands	506	-6
Aruba	297	-4	Costa Rica	225	0
Ascension Island	247	0	Côte d'Ivoire	385	+1
Australia	61	+8/+10	Croatia	33	-5
Austria	43	+1	Cuba	357	+2
Azerbaijan	994	+5	Cyprus	420	+1
Bahamas	1242	-5	Czech Republic	243	+2
Bahrain	973	+3	DR Congo	45	+1
Bangladesh	880	+6	Denmark	246	+5
Barbados	1246	-4	Diego Garcia	253	+3
Belarus	375	+2	Djibouti	1767	-4
Belgium	32	+1	Dominica	1809	-4
Belize	501	-6	Dominican Republic	593	-5
Benin	229	+1	Ecuador	20	+2
Bermuda	1441	-4	Egypt	503	-6
Bhutan	975	+6	El Salvador	240	+1
Bolivia	591	-4	Equatorial Guinea	291	+3
Bosnia-Herzegovina	387	+1	Eritrea	372	+2
Botswana	267	+2	Estonia	251	+3
Brazil	55	-3	Ethiopia	500	-4
Brunei	673	+8	Falkland Islands	298	0
Bulgaria	359	+2	Faroe Islands	679	+12
Burkina Faso	226	0	Fiji	358	+2
Burundi	257	+2	Finland	33	+1
Cambodia	855	+7	France	594	-3
Cameroon	237	+1	French Guiana	689	-10
Canada	1	-3½/-8	French Polynesia	241	+1
Cape Verde	238	-1	Gabon	220	0
Cayman Islands	1345	-5	Gambia	995	+4
Central African	236	+1	Georgia	49	+1

COUNTRY	DIALLING CODE	HOURS DIFF. FROM GMT	COUNTRY	DIALLING CODE	HOURS DIFF. FROM GMT
Germany	233	0	Liechtenstein	370	+2
Ghana	350	+1	Lithuania	352	+1
Gibraltar	30	+2	Luxembourg	853	+8
Greece	299	-4	Macao	389	+1
Greenland	1473	-4	Macedonia	261	+3
Grenada	590	-4	Madagascar	265	+2
Guadeloupe	1671	+10	Malawi	60	+8
Guam	502	-6	Malaysia	960	+5
Guatemala	224	0	Maldives	223	0
Guinea	245	0	Mali	356	+1
Guinea-Bissau	592	-4	Malta	692	+12
Guyana	509	-5	Marshall Islands	596	-4
Haiti	504	-6	Martinique	222	0
Honduras	852	+8	Mauritania	230	+4
Hong Kong	36	+1	Mauritius	269	+3
Hungary	354	0	Mayotte	52	-5/-7
Iceland	91	+5½	Mexico	691	+10/+11
India	62	+7/+9	Micronesia	373	+2
Indonesia	98	+3½	Moldova	377	+1
Iran	964	+3	Monaco	976	+8
Iraq	353	0	Mongolia	1664	-4
Ireland	972	+2	Montserrat	212	0
Israel	39	+1	Morocco	258	+2
Italy	1876	-5	Mozambique	95	+6½
Jamaica	81	+9	Myanmar	264	+1
Japan	962	+2	Namibia	674	+12
Jordan	7	+4/+6	Nauru	977	+5¾
Kazakhstan	254	+3	Nepal	31	+1
Kenya	686	+12	Netherlands	599	-4
Kiribati	965	+3	Netherlands Antilles	687	+11
Kuwait	996	+6	New Caledonia	64	+12
Kyrgyzstan	856	+7	New Zealand	505	-6
Laos	371	+2	Nicaragua	227	+1
Latvia	961	+2	Niger	234	+1
Lebanon	266	+2	Nigeria	683	-11
Lesotho	231	0	Niue	672	+11½
Liberia	218	+1	Norfolk Island	1670	+10
Libya	423	+1	Northern Marianas	850	+9

INTERNATIONAL INFORMATION

COUNTRY	DIALLING CODE	HOURS DIFF. FROM GMT	COUNTRY	DIALLING CODE	HOURS DIFF. FROM GMT
North Korea	47	+1	South Korea	34	+1
Norway	968	+4	Spain	94	+6
Oman	92	+5	Sri Lanka	249	+2
Pakistan	680	+9	Sudan	597	-3
Palau	507	-5	Suriname	268	+2
Panama	675	+10	Swaziland	46	+1
Papua New Guinea	595	-4	Sweden	41	+1
Paraguay	51	-5	Switzerland	963	+2
Peru	63	+8	Syria	886	+8
Philippines	48	+1	Taiwan	992	+6
Poland	351	0	Tajikistan	255	+3
Portugal	1787	4	Tanzania	66	+7
Puerto Rico	974	+3	Thailand	228	0
Qatar	262	+4	Togo	676	+13
Réunion	40	+2	Tonga	1868	-4
Romania	7	+2/+11	Trinidad and Tobago	216	+1
Russian Federation	250	+2	Tunisia	90	+2
Rwanda	290	0	Turkey	993	+5
St Helena	1869	-4	Turkmenistan	1649	-5
St Kitts and Nevis	1758	-4	Turks and Caicos Islands	688	+12
St Lucia	508	-3	Tuvalu	256	+3
St Pierre and Miquelon			Uganda	380	+2
St Vincent and	1784	-4	Ukraine	971	+4
the Grenadines	685	-11	United Arab Emirates	44	0
Samoa	378	+1	United Kingdom	1	-5/-10
San Marino	239	0	United States of	598	-3
São Tomé and Principe	966	+3	America	998	+5
Saudi Arabia	221	0	Uruguay	678	+11
Senegal	381	+1	Uzbekistan	58	-4
Serbia and Montenegro	248	+4	Vanuatu	84	+7
Seychelles	232	0	Venezuela	1284	-4
Sierra Leone	65	+8	Vietnam	1340	-4
Singapore	421	+1	Virgin Islands (UK)	681	+12
Slovakia	386	+1	Virgin Islands (US)	967	+3
Slovenia	677	+11	Wallis and Futuna	381	+1
Solomon Islands	252	+3	Yemen	260	+2
Somalia	27	+2	Yugoslavia	263	+2
South Africa	82	+9	Zambia		
			Zimbabwe		

CONVERSION TABLES

CENTIMETRES TO INCHES

cm		inches
2.54	1	0.39
5.08	2	0.79
7.62	3	1.81
10.1	4	1.57
12.7	5	1.97
15.2	6	2.36
17.8	7	2.76
20.3	8	3.15
22.9	9	3.54
25.4	10	3.94
27.9	11	4.33
30.4	12	4.72

LITRES TO GALLONS

litres		gallons
4.5	1	0.22
9.1	2	0.44
13.6	3	0.66
18.2	4	0.88
22.7	5	1.10
27.3	6	1.32
31.8	7	1.54
36.4	8	1.76
40.9	9	1.98
45.5	10	2.20

MEN'S SUITS AND OVERCOATS

American	British	Continental
36	36	46
38	38	48
40	40	50
42	42	52
44	44	54

MEN'S SHOES

American	British	Continental
8	7½	41
9	8½	42.5
10	9½	44
11	10½	45
12	11½	46
13	12	47.5

METRES TO FEET

metres		feet
0.30	1	3.3
0.61	2	6.6
0.91	3	9.8
1.22	4	13.1
1.52	5	16.4
1.83	6	19.7
2.13	7	23.0
2.44	8	26.2
2.74	9	29.5
3.05	10	32.8

CELSIUS TO FAHRENHEIT

l'c	l'f
-10	14
-5	23
0	32
5	41
10	50
15	59
20	68
25	77
30	86
35	95
40	104
45	113
50	122

MEN'S SHIRTS

American	British	Continental
14	14	36
14½	14½	37
15	15	38
15½	15½	39
16	16	41
16½	16½	42
17	17	43

KILOGRAMS TO POUNDS

kg		lb
0.45	1	2.2
0.91	2	4.4
1.36	3	6.6
1.81	4	8.8
2.27	5	11.0
2.72	6	13.2
3.18	7	15.4
3.63	8	17.6
4.08	9	19.8
4.54	10	22.0

KILOMETRES TO MILES

km	miles
10	6.2
20	12.4
30	18.6
40	24.9
50	31.1
60	37.3
70	43.5
80	49.5
90	55.9
100	62.1

WOMEN'S SUITS AND DRESSES

American	British	Continental
6	8	36
8	10	38
10	12	40
12	14	42
14	16	44
16	18	46
18	20	48

WOMEN'S SHOES

American	British	Continental
6	3¼	36
7	4½	37.5
8	5½	38.5
9	6½	40
10	7½	42

USEFUL ADDRESSES

'Woodhall Spa' (detail), LNER poster, 1923–47.
Artwork by Frank Newbould.

USEFUL ADDRESSES

USEFUL ADDRESSES

'The Coronation', LNER poster, 1938. Artwork by Frank H. Mason.